Word List

Read the following words:*

go	like	to
read	house	for
come	work	school
	love	

Before administering this Placement Test, turn to page 11 and read the instructions for the test.

*Instructor reads the directions.

SECTION 1
Things People Say About Reading and Being Back in School

I was afraid to go back to school. But I went back anyway. And I have learned many things. Did you know that one of the U.S. presidents learned to read when he was older? Or that 1 out of 10 people cannot read?

I have read some books. I have made many friends. Going to adult school was good for me.

You have to do 3 things to become a good reader. You have to 1) read, 2) read, and 3) read. That is what worked for me.

When I was a little kid, I did not think reading was important. Not at all. And I did not read. My first teacher was a man. He used to get mad at me and yell. One time he almost hit me. That did not make me like reading.

Then I had some women teachers. Most of them were OK. If they did not make me read, I sat quietly. But I did not learn anything that way.

When I went to high school, Miss Kits was my reading teacher. She was 25 and good looking. She used to tell stories. She played music. And I loved her. She said read. And I would read, read, read. All that reading made me into a good reader. That is how it worked for me.

I am working with someone on my reading. He is not a teacher. But he knows what he is doing. I am learning quickly. I feel good about the time I spend with him.

SECTION 2
How Exercise Changed My Life

by Rick Long

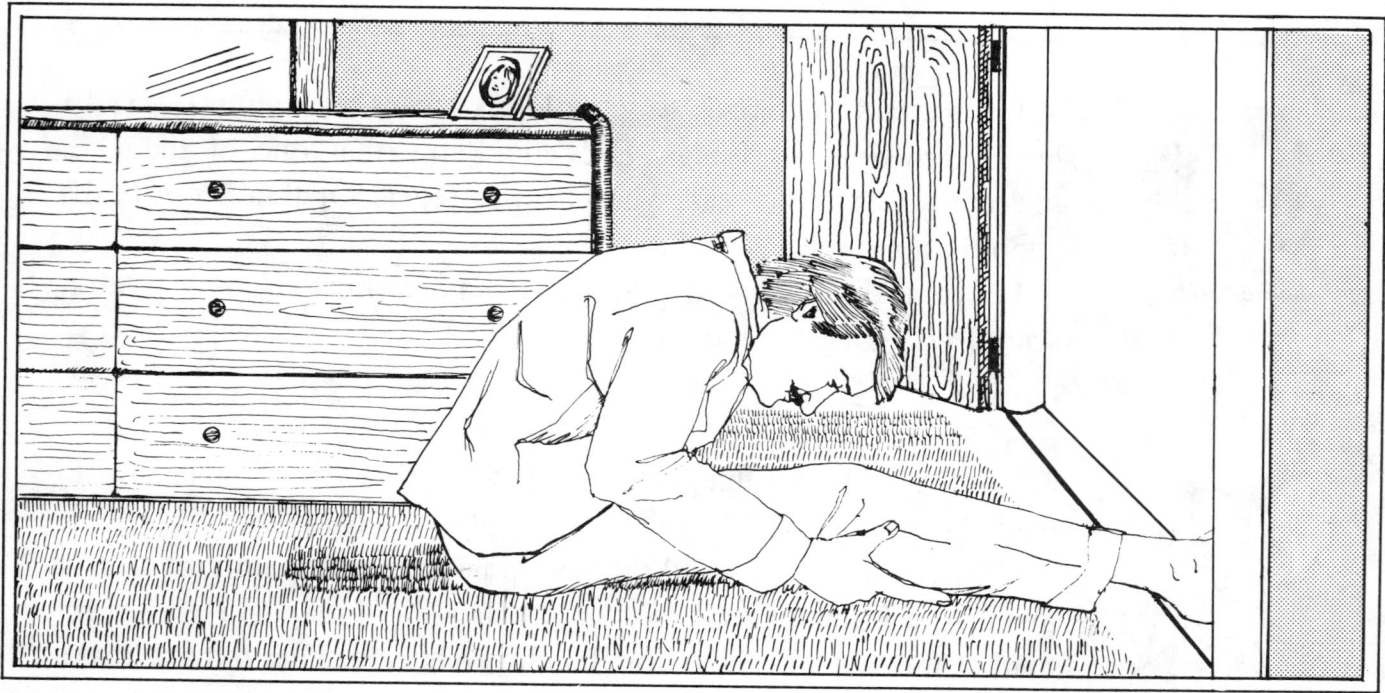

I used to have a weight problem. I am not kidding. I have a sales job. I don't get any exercise at work. And I did not exercise on my own. I like to read the newspaper. So sometimes I would pick up a paper. But that was all the exercise I got! And I used to eat sweets all day.

Again and again friends told me that I had to change my ways. I knew that they were trying to help me. But I was not interested. I just was not ready. I invented 100 ways to get out of exercising. Then one day I got locked out of my house. I could not fit through a window to get back in. I saw what was happening to me. And I did not like it. Right then and there I decided to change my life.

I have done just that. I have changed in 2 big ways. I no longer eat things that have a lot of calories. And I have been exercising 2 hours a day. When I get up, I do 100 sit-ups. Then I am out on the city streets jogging before it is even light.

I have been exercising for 2 years now. And I will not kid you. Sometimes exercising is hard. Most of the time it is lonely. But sometimes it is fun. I work out with friends 1 or 2 nights and we always have a good time.

Exercise is good in other ways too. Many people have told me that I look much younger. I feel different. Now my clothes fit right. And I feel safer too. I am very happy about losing weight. But sometimes I don't believe it. I have gone through a lot. But sometimes I think that I still have a weight problem.

Things to Think About*

What do you think of people who exercise 2 hours a day?

Could you exercise for 2 hours a day? Do you have the time?

Do you want to exercise for 2 hours a day?

Why does Rick still think that he has a weight problem?

---
*These can be the focus for discussion after reading the passage.

SECTION 3

Laid Off: My Story

by Tom King

I used to work in a factory making plastic booths. These booths were used in 5 and 10 cent stores for taking pictures. I liked my work but about four years back I was laid off. I have seen some hard times but things really got bad then. During that time, my life was like a bad dream. Everything looked ugly to me. And everything sounded bad. I was always angry. That's because I did not have enough money saved. And I hated being poor.

Things got bad at home too. I had always thought it was the husband's job to make money. But my wife saw things differently. She went out and got a job. She worked a cash register in a little shop. That hurt me as much as losing my job. We almost got divorced over that one. But once I saw it was necessary to let her help, it worked out O.K. Today we respect each other even more than we did in the past. I know that she is a beautiful person on the inside *and* the outside.

And that's not the only thing that has worked out. When I was first laid off, I thought about getting another factory job. But I found something much better. Someone from my church called me up with a really good idea. He said that the closest car parts store was too far away. He wanted me to start one here. Well that's just what I did. I also sell oil and new and used tools.

It took some doing, but the store is going great. Word got around that I sell things cheap. A lot of the credit also goes to my wife and two kids. The three of them run the store around the clock. That's right, we never close.

My sons have helped me in other ways too. I was never too good at spelling or reading. One of my sons takes care of all the charge card forms for me. He also has a good head for numbers, so he acts as my bookkeeper. My other son is an artist. He finished a sculpture of a car, and we put it in the store window. That has made my place even more well known.

And the future? Well, my credit with the bank is really good. I have been thinking of starting another store. It will not be too soon though. I have to find some good land, and that may take most of next year.

Before you go, I have to tell you something that I have learned. You may want to remember it. You can never *really* know what to expect from life. When I was laid off, I became very depressed. I did not know then that it was the best thing that ever happened to me. You just never know how something will work out. Nothing in life is a sure thing.

Things to Think About*

About how old do you think Tom is?

Do you think he is happy with his life? Why or why not?

Tom says, "Nothing in life is a sure thing." What do you think about this?

---
*These can be the focus for discussion after reading.

Phonics Test*

Level 1: Consonant Sounds

Say the sound made by each of the following letters.

    b   f   k   l   n   p   r   t

    v   y   d   h   m   j   q   s

    w   z

These two consonants make two sounds. Make both of the sounds made by these letters.

    c   g

Level 2: Short vowels **a** and **i**

Read these nonsense syllables.

    ab   af   az

    im   ik   ip

Level 3: Short vowels **e**, **o**, and **u**

Read these nonsense syllables.

    uf   un   ut

    ob   ol   om

    el   ep   ek

---

*Directions are read by the instructor. In levels 2–5, explain to the student that nonsense syllables are used to determine whether or not they know the sounds made by the combinations of letters.

Level 4: Long Vowels

Read these nonsense syllables.

ake	ope	ine	ule	eal
eet	oap	ain	ay	ite

Level 5: Consonant Blends and Digraphs

Read these nonsense syllables.

blap	clet	flet	glod	plu
bren	cril	drat	frug	graz
whik	thof	chug	chen	shib
slan	pren	shof	tra	

Placement Test Overview

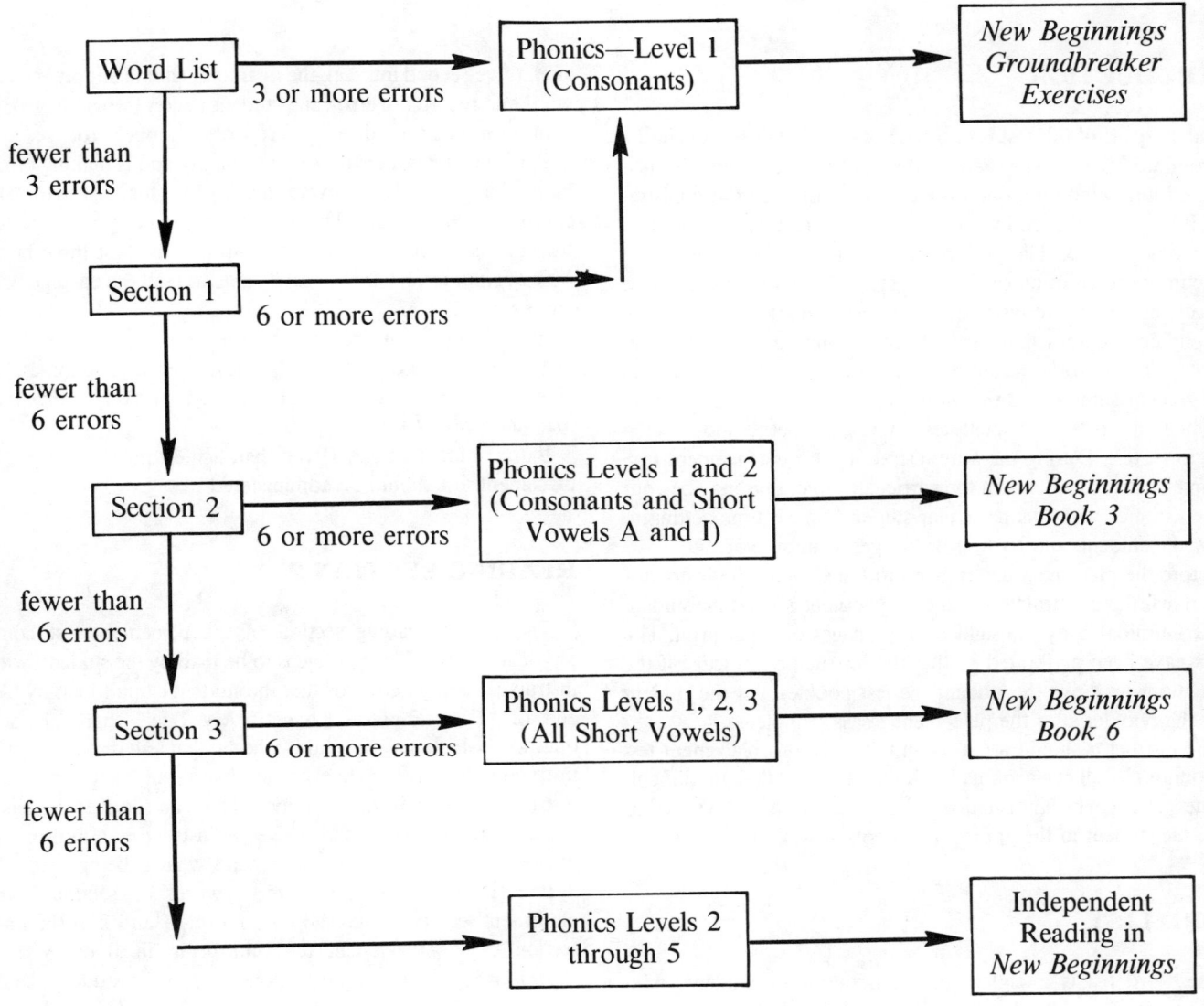

── **Points to Remember** ──

A word that is misread more than once is only considered one error.

The test atmosphere should be as relaxed and positive as possible.

New Beginnings in Reading—Placement Test
Instructions

INTRODUCTION

The purpose of this test is to place low-level adult readers in the appropriate book in *New Beginnings*. This test has been designed to be administered on a one-to-one basis. For ease of administration, it has been divided into four parts: three reading sections and one phonics section. The three reading sections, which should take a maximum of 20 minutes to administer, will enable you to place students either in Groundbreaker Exercises, Book 3, or Book 6. The phonics section will indicate specific sounds and word families that need extra work. Before beginning the actual placement test, each student should read the word list on the title page.

While this is a placement test, it really doesn't look like a traditional test. During the administration of this placement test, feel free to stop to talk about the particular topic. This may be your first encounter with this particular student. Spend time getting to know the student, and let him or her get to know you.

Before the placement test is given to the student, the instructor should tear these instructions out of the booklet, so that the student is not intimidated by the sight of three pages of small print. The pages have been perforated so that the instructor can tear off the instructions and give the student the test booklet. Let the student keep the booklet after the placement test is completed.

The instructor should use a second copy of this placement test to monitor a student's reading, marking the words that are difficult for the student. This information is important, as it will be used to place the student in the appropriate book in *New Beginnings*.

WORD LIST

The word list is intended to screen out those students who would be frustrated by the placement test because of their lack of reading ability. If a particular student makes three or more errors on the list of ten words, the placement test would be too frustrating for the student. It is recommended that this student do only level 1 of the phonics test and then be placed in the first lesson in *New Beginnings—Groundbreaker Exercises*.

READING SECTION 1

Section 1 of the placement test consists of stories of several people who are returning to school to learn to read. The person that is administering this test should read the title and have the student read the stories.

As the student reads through section 1, the instructor should discreetly record the words that the student misses. The instructor can use a second copy of this placement test to mark the words that the student misses. If the student is unable to identify a word after a five-second interval, the instructor should supply the correct word and record the error. If a student makes the same error more than once, this should only be recorded as one error.

If a student has a great deal of difficulty and is making errors on more than one out of every ten words, the instructor should complete the reading. The instructor should point out to the student that after the student has finished the first three books in *New Beginnings*, he or she will be able to read the passage without any help.

If the student misses six or more words on section 1 of the placement test, he or she should do level one of the phonics section of the placement test and be placed in *New Beginnings—Groundbreaker Exercises*.

If the student makes fewer than six errors, section 2 of this placement test should be administered.

READING SECTION 2

The second reading section of the placement test concerns physical exercise. The passage is to be read by the student, with the instructor supplying words that the student cannot identify. At the end of "How Exercise Changed My Life," there are several questions which may be read by the student and discussed with the instructor. Since it is likely that this is the first time that an instructor and a student have met, these can serve as the basis for a conversation. They can also give the instructor an informal sense of the student's ability to comprehend what is being read.

If a student misses six or more words on section 2 of the placement test, he or she should do levels 1 and 2 of the phonics section of the placement test and begin in Book 3 of *New Beginnings*. It is important to point out to the student that after Books 3, 4, and 5 have been completed, he or she should be able to read this passage without any difficulty.

If a student misses fewer than 6 words, section 3 of this placement test should be administered.

READING SECTION 3

The third reading section of the placement test discusses the results of being laid off. The passage is to be read by the student, with the instructor supplying any words the student cannot identify. At the end of the passage there are several questions which may serve as an informal check of the student's ability to comprehend what is being read.

If a student misses six or more words on section 3 of the placement test, he or she should do levels 1, 2, and 3 of the phonics section of the placement test and begin instruction with Book 6 of *New Beginnings*. If the student had considerable difficulty in reading section 3, the student should be told that after working through Books 6, 7, and 8 of *New Beginnings*, he or she will be able to read this passage without any difficulty.

If a student has missed fewer than six words in section 3, *New Beginnings* may be used as independent reading material. The